WORD WIZARD

Literacy Skills and Activities

GILL SKILLS

SENIOR INFANTS

Jane O'Loughlin

GILL EDUCATION

Contents

How to Use this Book

Themes and planning

Word Wizard Junior Infants and *Senior Infants* follow a thematic approach, with most themes spanning two units (four-weeks' work), allowing for easy planning. Learning outcomes from the new Language Curriculum are referenced on each page.

Aistear

These activity books link closely with Aistear. A comprehensive Aistear plan is provided for each month, in addition to integrating the theme throughout the corresponding unit wherever possible. The plan lists a wide range of station activities, poems, action rhymes, songs and suitable YouTube links.

Free printable Aistear resources are also available online, with a wide range of resources for each theme.

Engaging oral language activities

Each month begins with an oral language activity based on the Aistear theme. Detailed teaching notes are available online and may serve as preparatory activities for setting up a similar role-play area within Aistear. Each oral language lesson covers associated vocabulary, explores possible role-play scenarios and discusses suggested conversational language as well as brainstorming resources for setting up a role-play area.

Flexible phonics approach

In *Word Wizard Senior Infants*, both the alphabet and digraphs are covered in quick succession. As some schools do not cover digraphs at Junior Infant level, a set of corresponding worksheets is available as a teaching resource online. These may be used as an introductory activity before progressing with the phonics sections in the activity book. Note that all sounds are covered by Unit 9. The remaining units focus on a range of blending activities integrated with the unit's theme.

Please note that sounds are taught in the following order:

Letters		Digraphs
s, a, t, p	h, o, l, b	ai, oa, ie, ee
i, n, m, d	u, f, j, v	or, ng, oo (book), oo (tooth)
e, c, k, g, r	z, x, y, w, qu	ou, oi, ue, er, ar
		ch, sh, th, wh

Genre writing

Word Wizard Junior Infants covers the genres of recount, writing to socialise, report and narrative. *Word Wizard Senior Infants* covers the genres of recount, procedure, narrative, report and poetry.

Genre writing is integrated with the various themes throughout each book and pupils are exposed to each genre through a range of modelled, shared and independent-writing activities following best practice. Each activity is accompanied by online teaching notes and templates for use on the interactive whiteboard. YouTube links are also included for use as a stimulus wherever appropriate. Some genres are further consolidated through play and may be found referenced as activities within Aistear plans.

Revision and assessment

Revision activities feature regularly throughout both activity books.

A self-assessment feature appears below all phonics and handwriting activities:

How do I feel about my work today?

Two assessment units focusing on phonics are provided at the end of the second and third terms.

Activity directions

Where activity directions are required by the teacher, such as in sight-word and auditory discrimination activities, an animal character appears at the bottom of the page with the directions discreetly enclosed in a speech bubble.

Navigating the online resources

In order to help you navigate the online resources, a number of teacher's symbols (explained below) appear on the right-hand side of pages throughout the activity book.

Key to online resource symbols	
	Oral language Indicates that a detailed oral language activity is available online.
	Discussion genre text Indicates that an excerpt from another text, highlighting features of a particular genre, and accompanying teacher's notes are available online.
	Modelled or shared writing experience Indicates that a modelled writing activity with accompanying teacher's notes is available online.
	Printable Indicates that a printable such as a writing template is available online.
	Vocabulary mat Indicates that an editable vocabulary mat is available for use on the interactive whiteboard.
	Aistear plan and resources Indicates that a comprehensive Aistear plan with accompanying resources is available online.

The Secretary's Office

Oral Language

A Talk about the picture.

- postwoman
- keys
- fire drill
- Welcome
- opening hours
  open 9 o'clock
  closed 3 o'clock
- buzzer
- bell
- telephone
- phone numbers
- A - Z
- secretary
- first aid

Strand: Oral Language **Elements:** Understanding LO 5, 6, 7; Exploring and Using LO 8, 9, 14

Phonics s, a, t, p

A Can you match each picture to the correct sound?

s

a

ABCDEF
GHIJKLM
NOPQRST
UVWXYZ

t

p

B Look at each picture. Tick the correct word.

as	tap	pat
sat	pat	at

How do I feel about my work today?

Strand: Reading Element: Understanding LO 5

7

Handwriting | s, a, t, p

A Trace and write the letters.

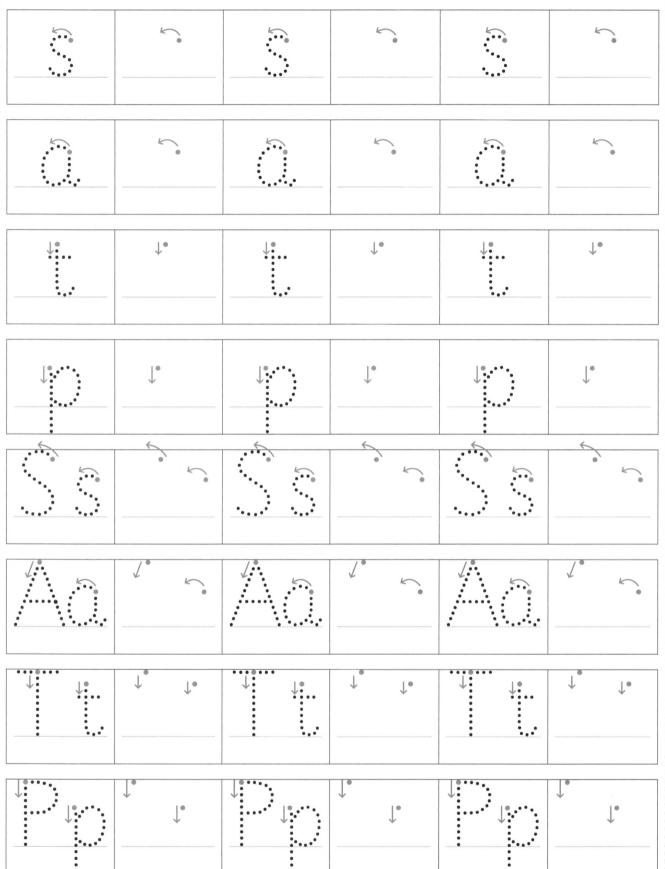

Strand: Writing Element: Exploring and Using LO 9

Sight Words the, to, and, he, a, I

A Listen to your teacher.

 the  and  to 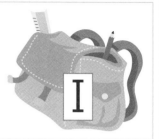 I

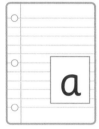 a 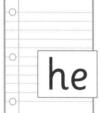 he 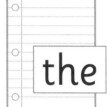 the 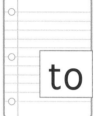 to

 I  and  he  a

 a  the  he  to

 a  and  I  to

- Look at the school bags. Ring the word 'and'. Ring the word 'I'.
- Look at the pages. Ring the word 'he'. Ring the word 'the'.
- Look at the bins. Ring the word 'a'. Ring the word 'I'.
- Look at the lunch boxes. Ring the word 'the'. Ring the word 'to'.
- Look at the books. Ring the word 'and'. Ring the word 'I'.

Phonics i, n, m, d

A Can you match each picture to the correct sound?

i

n

m

d

B Read each word. Match it to the correct picture.

pan

tin

nap

pin

How do I feel about my work today?

Strand: Reading **Element:** Understanding LO 5

Handwriting | i, n, m, d

A Trace and write the letters.

i		i		i	
n		n		n	
m		m		m	
d		d		d	
Ii		Ii		Ii	
Nn		Nn		
Mm		Mm		
Dd		Dd		

How do I feel about my work today?

Strand: Writing **Element:** Exploring and Using LO 9

Writing Genre – Parts of a Recount

A Look at the Word Wizard below. Can you tell your news using when, who, where, what and why?

My News

Where?

Who?

What?

When?

Why?

B Ask the news teller some questions about their news.

C Practise every day. Try using 'Think, Pair, Share'.

Strand: Oral Language **Element:** Understanding LO 4; Exploring and Using LO 8, 9, 11

School

Oral Language – Odd One Out

A Ring the odd one out. Can you say why?

1.				
2.				
3.				
4.				
5.				

Phonics | e, c, k, g, r

A Can you match each picture to the correct sound?

e

c

k

g

r

B Read each word. Match it to the correct picture.

sit

mat

pen

red

How do I feel about my work today?

14

Strand: Reading **Element:** Understanding LO 5

Handwriting e, c, k, g, r

A Trace and write the letters.

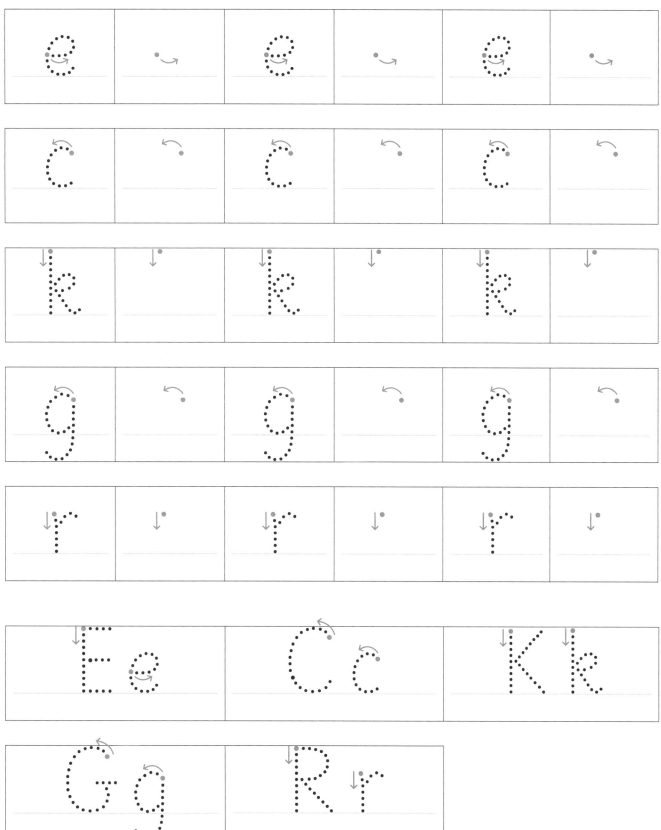

Strand: Writing **Element:** Exploring and Using LO 9

Sight Words you, it, of, in, was, said

A Listen to your teacher.

 said  in  was  of

 it  in  you  said

 you  was  of  it

 in  said  was  you

 it  of  in  said

- Look at the children. Ring the word 'in'. Ring the word 'said'.
- Look at the teachers. Ring the word 'you'. Ring the word 'said'.
- Look at the cleaners. Put an X on the word 'was'. Put an X on the word 'it'.
- Look at the secretaries. Put an X on the word 'you'. Put an X on the word 'was'.
- Look at the lollipop people. Put an X on the word 'said'. Put an X on the word 'of'.

Strand: Reading **Element:** Understanding LO 5

Phonics – Revision | s, a, t, p, i, n, m, d, e, c, k, g, r |

A Can you match each picture to the correct sound?

s
a
t
p
i
n

m
d
e
c
g
r

B Read each word. Match it to the correct picture.

tin

peg

ran

bag

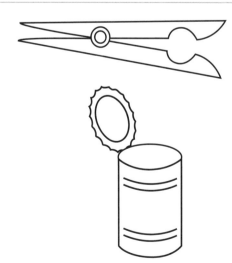

How do I feel about my work today?

Strand: Reading **Element:** Understanding LO 5

Handwriting – Revision

A Trace and write the letters.

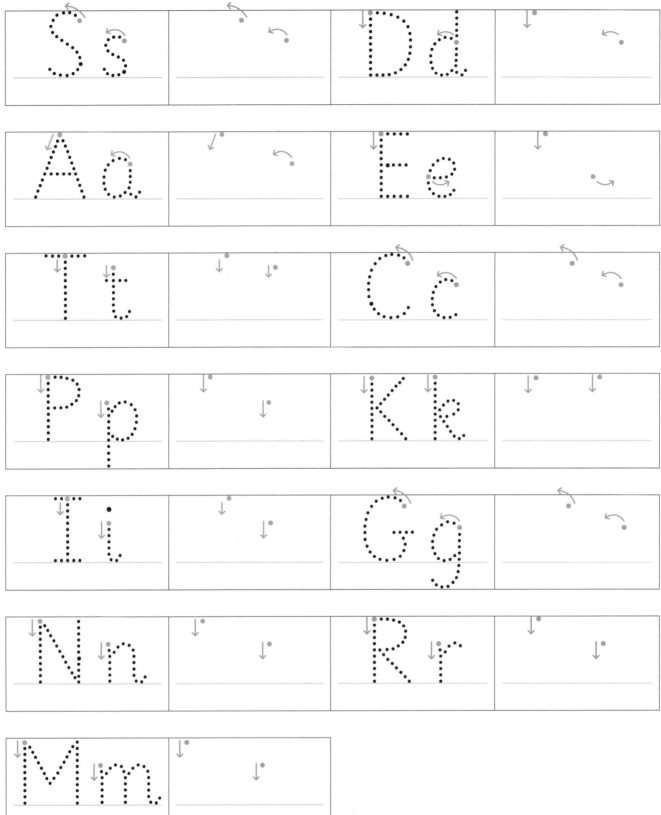

My best letter: My trickiest letter:

How do I feel about my work today?

Strand: Writing **Element:** Exploring and Using LO 9

Writing Genre – Modelled Writing

A In pairs, tell your news to your partner. Then, tell your partner's news to the class.

B Draw your news below and add labels.

My News Plan

When?

Who?

Where?

What?

Why?

Strand: Oral Language **Elements:** Understanding LO 4; Exploring and Using LO 11
Strand: Writing **Elements:** Communicating LO 1; Understanding LO 3, 4, 5; Exploring and Using LO 5, 6, 7, 8

The Post Office

3

Oral Language

A Talk about the picture.

A

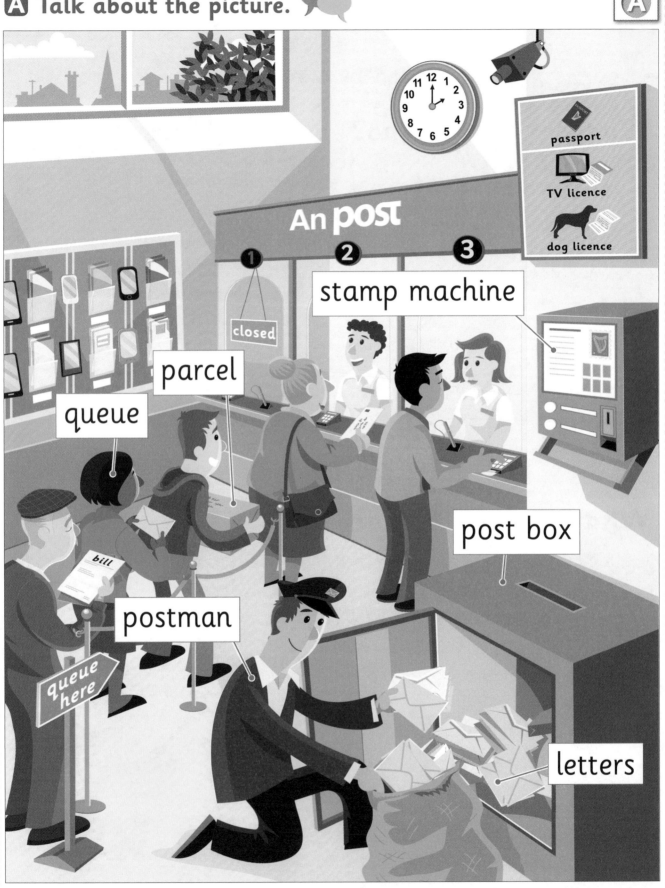

passport

TV licence

dog licence

An **post**

1 2 3

closed

stamp machine

parcel

queue

post box

bill

postman

queue here

letters

Strand: Oral Language **Elements:** Understanding LO 5, 6, 7; Exploring and Using LO 8, 9, 14

Phonics h, o, l, b

A Can you match each picture to the correct sound?

h

o

l

b

B Read each phrase. Match it to the correct picture.

a big cat

a red pen

a sad man

How do I feel about my work today?

Strand: Reading **Element:** Understanding LO 5

21

Handwriting h, o, l, b

A Trace and write the letters.

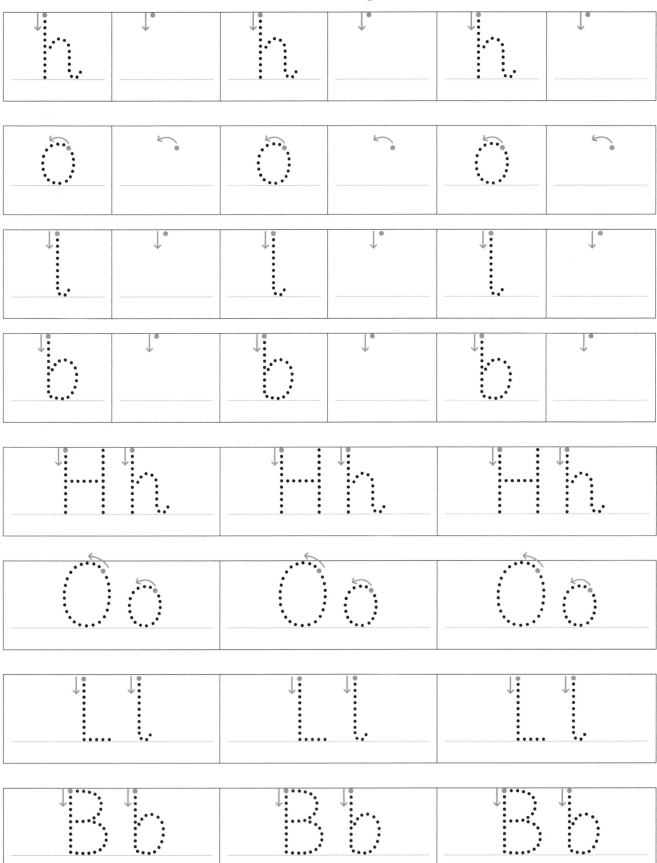

How do I feel about my work today?

Strand: Writing Element: Exploring and Using LO 9

Sight Words | his, that, she, for, on, they

A Listen to your teacher.

 that  for  she  on

 they  his  for  on

 she  they  that  his

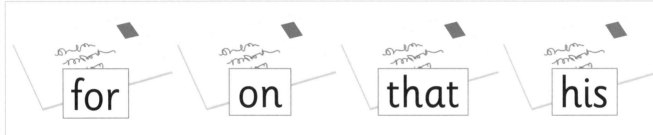 for · on · that · his

 the · that · they · to

- Look at the postmen. Ring the word 'she'. Ring the word 'that'.
- Look at the parcels. Ring the word 'they'. Ring the word 'on'.
- Look at the post boxes. Put an X on the word 'his'. Put an X on the word 'that'.
- Look at the envelopes. Put an X on the word 'on'. Put an X on the word 'for'.
- Look at the post vans. Put an X on the word 'to'. Put an X on the word 'the'.

Phonics u, f, j, v

A Can you match each picture to the correct sound?

u

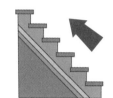

f

j

v

B Read each phrase. Match it to the correct picture.

a red bus

a fat cat

a big jet

a hot pan

How do I feel about my work today?

Strand: Reading **Element:** Understanding LO 5

Handwriting u, f, j, v

A Trace and write the letters.

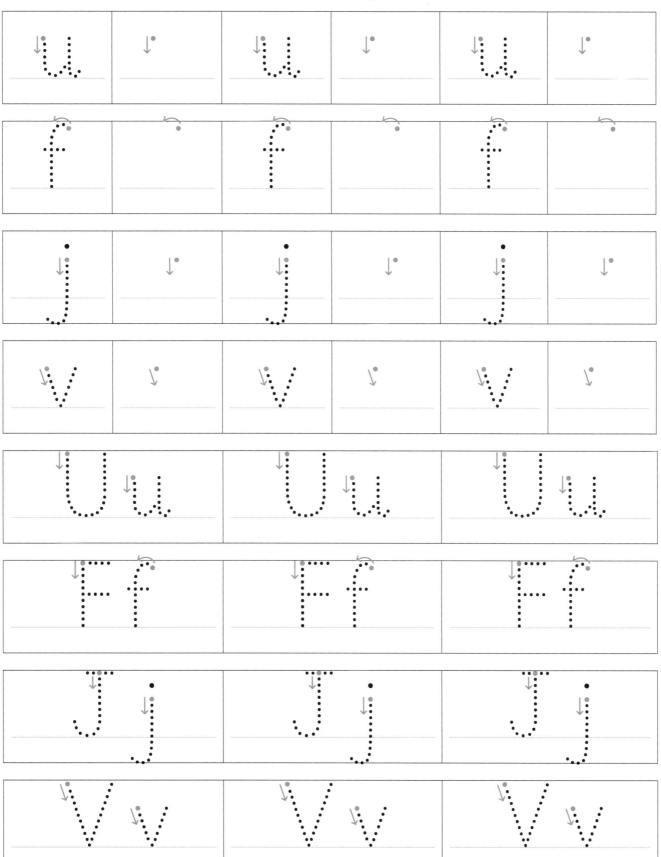

How do I feel about my work today? ☺ ○ 😐 ○ ☹ ○

Strand: Writing Element: Exploring and Using LO 9

Writing Genre – Shared Writing

A My news

Draw your news below and write about it. If the postman visited your class, you might like to write about this instead.

My News Plan

When?

Who?

Where?

What?

Why?

B Write your news by yourself.

_____

_____

Strand: Oral Language **Elements:** Understanding LO 4; Exploring and Using LO 11
Strand: Writing **Elements:** Communicating LO 1; Understanding LO 3, 4, 5; Exploring and Using LO 5, 6, 7, 8

The Postman

Oral Language – Rhyming Words

A Match the words that rhyme.

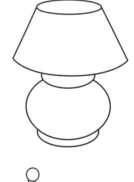

Phonics – Revision s, a, t, p, i, n, m, d, e

A Look at each picture. Write the sound that it begins with.

s   a   t   p   i   n   m   d   e

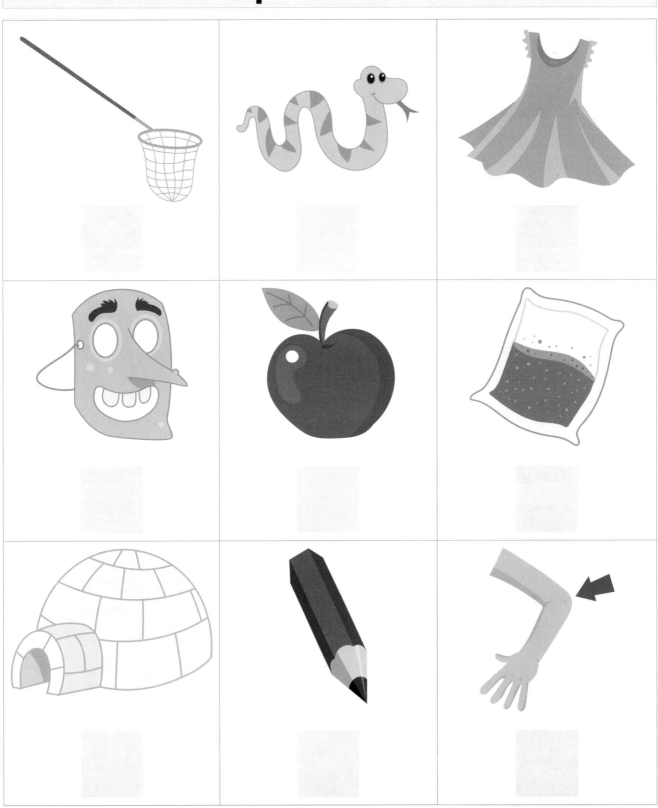

How do I feel about my work today? 🙂 ⚪ 😐 ⚪ ☹ ⚪

Strand: Reading Element: Understanding LO 5 Strand: Writing Element: Exploring and Using LO 9

Phonics – Revision | c, k, g, r, h, o, l, b, u, f, j, v

A Look at each picture. Write the sound that it begins with.

c k g r h o l b u f j v

How do I feel about my work today?

Strand: Reading **Element:** Understanding LO 5 **Strand:** Writing **Element:** Exploring and Using LO 9

Sight Words – Revision Phrases

A Read each phrase. Match it to the correct picture.

1. She was sad.

2. It was hot.

3. a hat for Dad

4. a cat in the bin

5. a dog and a pup

6. a man on a bus

Strand: Reading Element: Understanding LO 5

Handwriting – Revision

A Trace and write the letters.

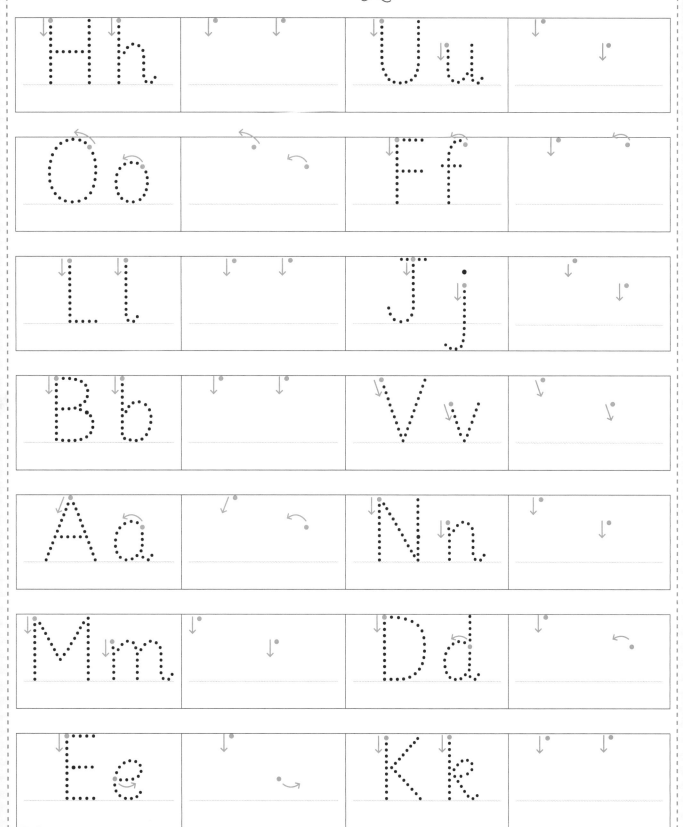

Hh		Uu	
O o		Ff	
Ll		Jj	
Bb		Vv	
Aa		Nn	
Mm		Dd	
Ee		Kk	

My best letter: My trickiest letter:

How do I feel about my work today?

Strand: Writing Element: Exploring and Using LO 9

Phonics – Revision

A Look at each picture. Tick the correct word.

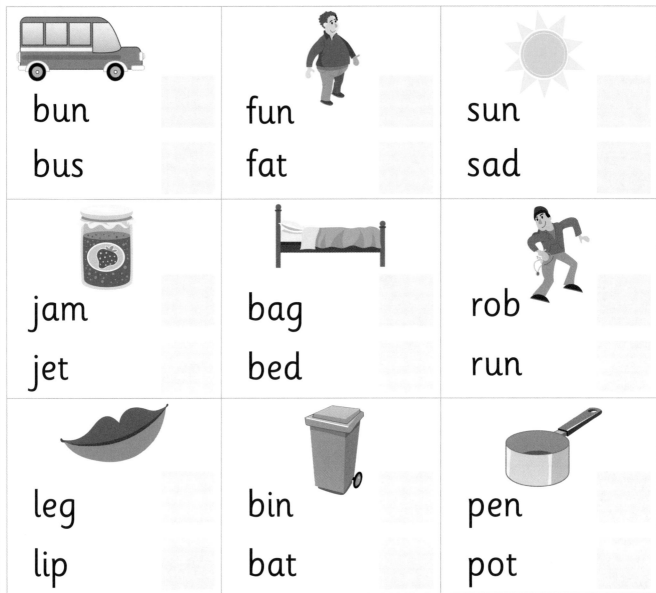

bun	fun	sun
bus	fat	sad
jam	bag	rob
jet	bed	run
leg	bin	pen
lip	bat	pot

B Read each phrase. Match it to the correct picture.

a fat dog

a sad vet

a red hat

How do I feel about my work today?

Strand: Reading **Element:** Understanding LO 5

Writing Genre – Independent Writing

A Write a letter to your friend telling them your news.

When?

Who?

Where?

What?

Why?

Dear   ,

From

Strand: Oral Language **Elements:** Understanding LO 4; Exploring and Using LO 11
Strand: Writing **Elements:** Communicating LO 1; Understanding LO 3, 4, 5; Exploring and Using LO 5, 6, 7, 8

33

The Coffee Shop

Oral Language

A Talk about the picture.

A

Strand: Oral Language **Elements:** Understanding LO 5, 6, 7; Exploring and Using LO 8, 9, 14

Phonics z, x, y, w, qu

A Can you match each picture to the correct sound?

z

x

y

w

qu

B Read each sentence. Match it to the correct picture.

The fox had a nap.

I had six jam buns.

The vet has a cat.

The bug ran on the log.

How do I feel about my work today?

Strand: Reading Element: Understanding LO 5

Handwriting z, x, y, w, qu

A Trace and write the letters.

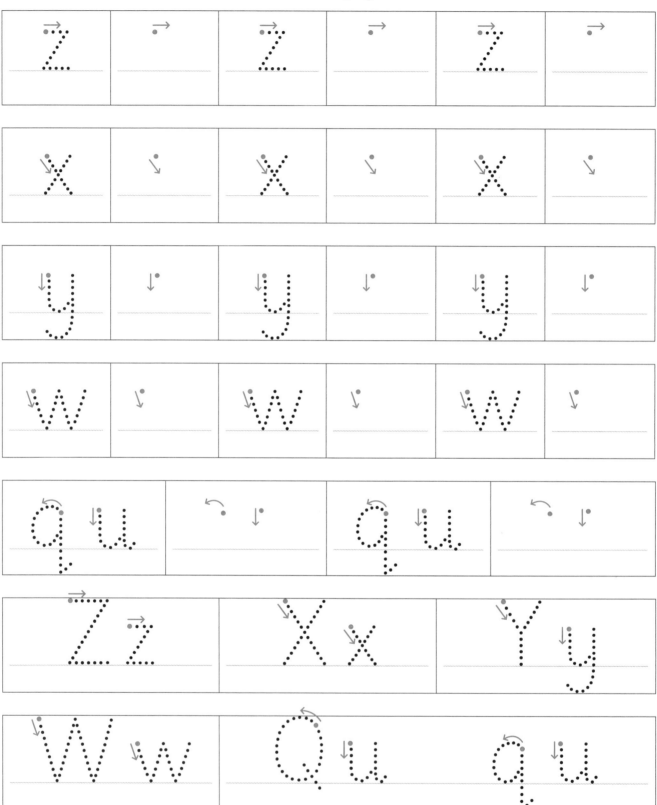

My best letter: ⬜   My trickiest letter: ⬜

How do I feel about my work today?

Strand: Writing **Element:** Exploring and Using LO 9

Sight Words but, had, at, him, with, up

A Listen to your teacher.

 at

 but

 up

 had

 him

 up

 with

 at

 up

 but

 had

 at

 him

 had

 with

 up

 him

 has

 had

 he

- Look at the teacups. Put a dot on the word 'up'. Put a dot on the word 'but'.
- Look at the cakes. Put a smiley face on the word 'at'. Put a smiley face on the word 'with'.
- Look at the cookies. Put a dot on the word 'but'. Put a dot on the word 'had'.
- Look at the glasses of orange juice. Put a smiley face on the word 'him'. Put a smiley face on the word 'with'.
- Look at the cupcakes. Put a smiley face on the word 'had'. Put a smiley face on the word 'he'.

Strand: Reading **Element:** Understanding LO 5

37

Phonics | ai, oa, ie, ee

A Can you match each picture to the correct sound?

ai

oa

ie

ee

B Read each sentence. Match it to the correct picture.

The pie is in the bin.

I put on my red coat.

Dad got his hair cut.

Tom had a bag of sweets.

How do I feel about my work today?

Strand: Reading Element: Understanding LO 5

Handwriting ai, oa, ie, ee

A Trace and write the letters.

ai	ai	ai	ai	ai	ai
ai					
oa	oa	oa	oa	oa	oa
oa					
ie	ie	ie	ie	ie	ie
ie					
ee	ee	ee	ee	ee	ee
ee					

How do I feel about my work today?

Writing Genre – Parts of a Procedure

A How to make play-dough ✏️

Can you remember how to make play-dough? Put the steps in order starting with number 1.

B In pairs, take turns telling your partner how to make play-dough. 💬

Strand: Oral Language **Element:** Understanding LO 7; Exploring and Using LO 13

The Waitress

6

Oral Language – Auditory Discrimination

A Listen to your teacher.

- Draw a box around the waitress who has a pencil and is wearing glasses.
- Ring the waitress who has a tray with a glass of orange juice.
- Draw a line under the waitress who has a pencil and is not wearing glasses.
- Put an X on the waitress who has a tray with a pot of tea.

Strand: Oral Language **Element:** Understanding LO 7

Phonics or, ng, oo (book), oo (tooth)

A Can you match each picture to the correct sound?

or

ng

oo

oo

B Read each sentence. Match it to the correct picture.

There was a storm.

Tess sat on the stool.

She had a big ring.

Look at the big ant!

How do I feel about my work today?

Strand: Reading **Element:** Understanding LO 5

Handwriting | or, ng, oo (book), oo (tooth)

A Trace and write the letters.

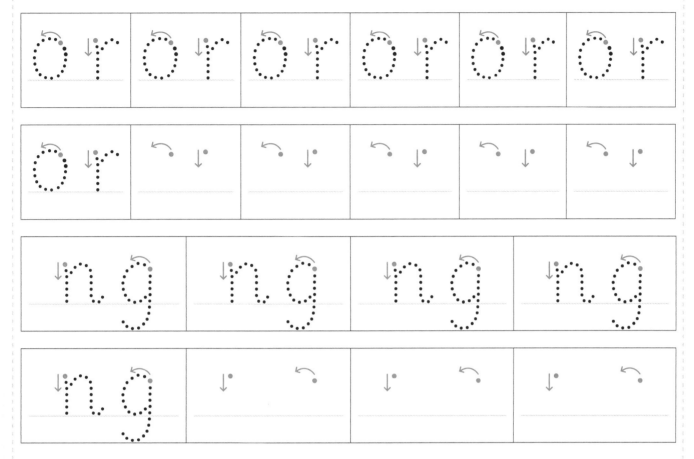

oo

> We can make the /u/ sound as in '**book**' or the /ue/ sound as in '**tooth**'.

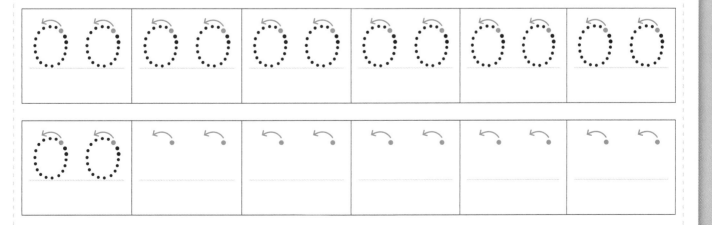

How do I feel about my work today?

Strand: Writing **Element:** Exploring and Using LO 9

Sight Words – Revision Phrases

A Play the game.

1

it was

you and I

2

I said

he was in

3

they had

she had a

4

it was up

he was at

5

that is it

get it for him

6

that was for

this and that

- Play the game in pairs. You will need 12 counters each and a die.
- The player who rolls the highest number goes first.
- Throw the die and read a phrase from the slice of cake with the number rolled. If read correctly, place your counter on the phrase.
- The player who covers all phrases first wins.
- Variation: Can you put the phrases in a sentence this time?

Strand: Reading **Element:** Understanding LO 5

Phonics ou, oi, ue, er, ar

A Can you match each picture to the correct sound?

ou

oi

ue

er

ar

B Read each sentence. Match it to the correct picture.

Sam got a letter.

 ... 7, 8, 9, 10

Mum has a blue hat.

I can count to ten.

Dad cut his arm.

How do I feel about my work today?

Strand: Reading Element: Understanding LO 5

Handwriting | ou, oi, ue, er, ar

A Trace and write the letters.

ou ou ou ou ou ou

ou

oi oi oi oi oi oi

oi

ue ue ue ue ue ue

ue

er er er er er er

er

ar ar ar ar ar ar

ar

How do I feel about my work today? 😊 ◯ 😐 ◯ ☹ ◯

Strand: Writing **Element:** Exploring and Using LO 9

Writing Genre – Modelled and Shared Writing

A How to make an orange drink

Tick what you need to make an orange drink. Then, label the picture for each step.

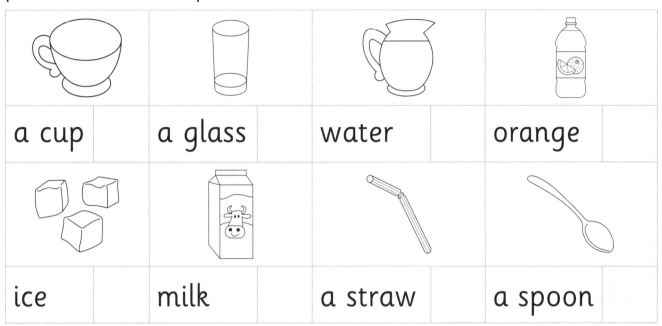

| a cup | a glass | water | orange |
| ice | milk | a straw | a spoon |

Steps:

1.

2.

3.

4.

B With your class, write about how you can make an orange drink.

Strand: Writing **Elements:** Communicating LO 1; Understanding LO 3, 4, 5; Exploring and Using LO 6

The Garda Station

Oral Language

A Talk about the picture.

Strand: Oral Language **Elements:** Understanding LO 5, 6, 7; Exploring and Using LO 8, 9, 14

Phonics – Revision   z, x, y, w, qu, ai, oa, ie, ee

A Look at each picture. Write the sound that you hear.

| z | x | y | w | qu | ai | oa | ie | ee |

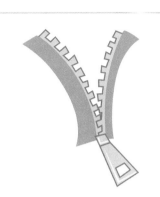

How do I feel about my work today?

Strand: Reading Element: Understanding LO 5 Strand: Writing Element: Exploring and Using LO 9

Phonics – Revision | or, ng, oo (book), oo (tooth), ou, oi, ue, er, ar

A Look at each picture. Write the sound that you hear.

| **or** | **ng** | **oo** | **oo** | **ou** | **oi** | **ue** | **er** | **ar** |

 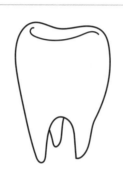 

  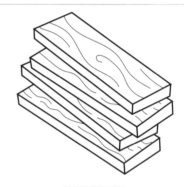

How do I feel about my work today?

Strand: Reading **Element:** Understanding LO 5 **Strand:** Writing **Element:** Exploring and Using LO 9

Handwriting – The Alphabet

A Trace and write the letters.

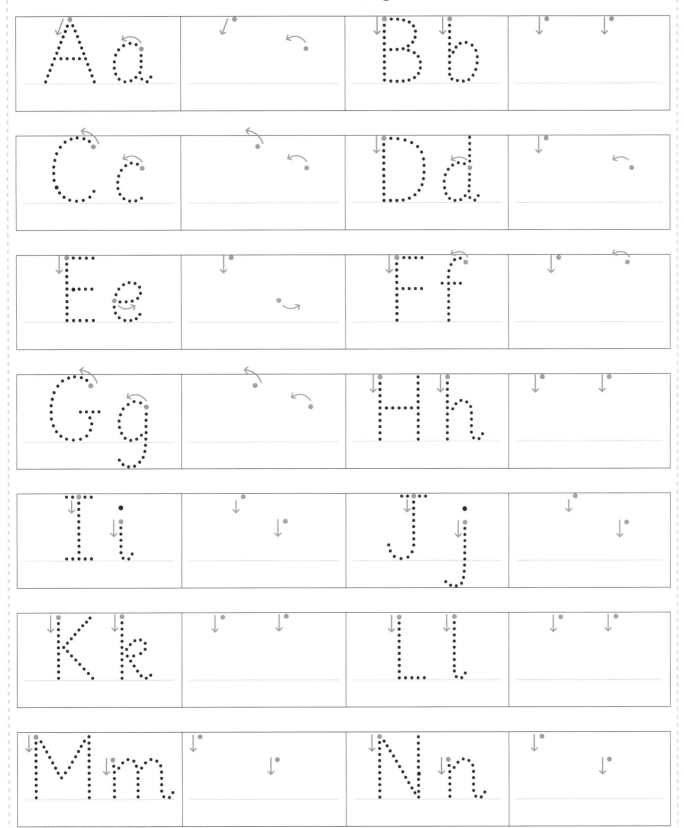

My best letter: My trickiest letter:

How do I feel about my work today?

Strand: Writing **Element:** Exploring and Using LO 9

Handwriting – The Alphabet

A Trace and write the letters.

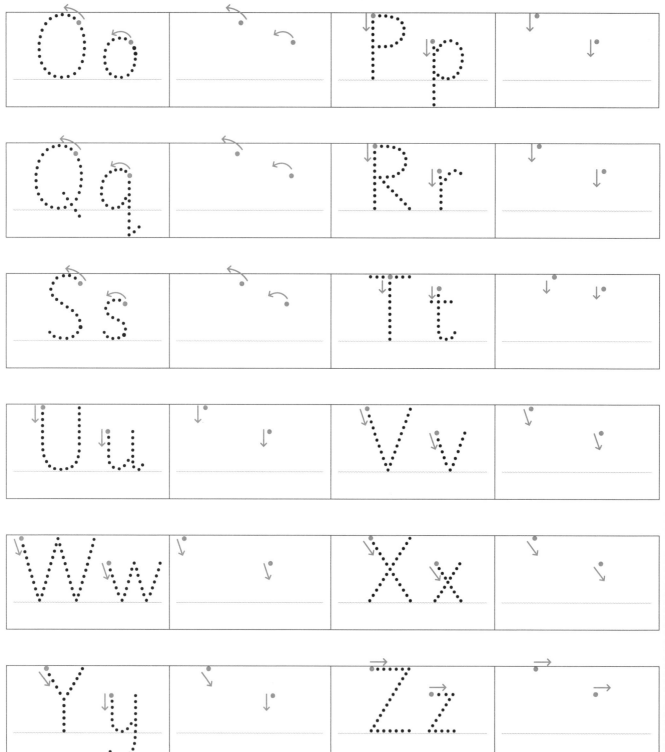

My best letter:    My trickiest letter:

How do I feel about my work today?

Strand: Writing **Element:** Exploring and Using LO 9

Sight Words – Revision Sentences

A Read each sentence. Fill in the correct word.

1.	The bee was _____ the hut.	it / in
2.	Look at him up _____ the roof.	on / a
3.	That is _____ car.	had / his
4.	She had a pup _____ a cat.	at / and
5.	Did you get the book _____ Sam?	for / of
6.	_____ got a bag of sweets.	him / He

Writing Genre – Independent Writing

A **How to make a cheese sandwich for Garda Tom**

Tick what you need to make a cheese sandwich. Then, label the pictures.

bread	butter	cheese	a jug
a knife	a plate	a cup	a lunch box

Steps:

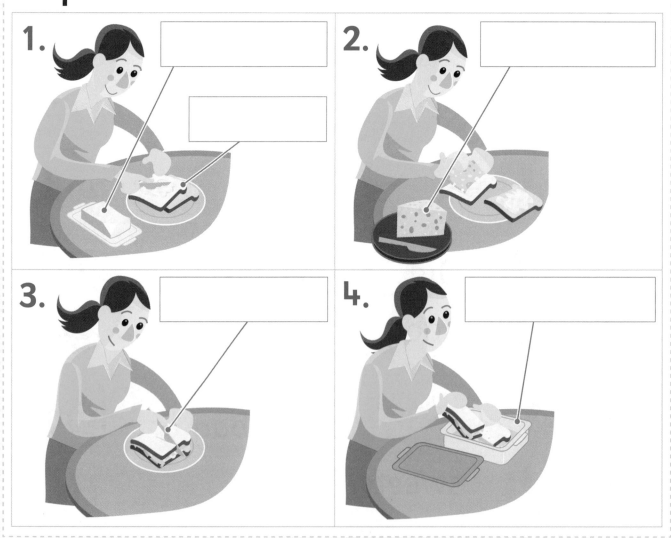

1.

2.

3.

4.

Strand: Writing **Elements:** Communicating LO 1; Understanding LO 3, 4, 5; Exploring and Using LO 6

Assessment

8

Phonics Assessment

A Look at each picture. Can you write the sound that it begins with?

s			m
a			d
t			e
p			c
i			k
n			g

How do I feel about my work today?

55

Phonics Assessment

A Look at each picture. Can you write the sound that it begins with?

Phonics Assessment

A Can you match each picture to the correct sound?

ie

ee

ai

or

ou

ar

oi

oo

oa

ng

oo

ue

qu

er

The Estate Agents

9

Oral Language

A Talk about the picture.

Strand: Oral Language **Elements:** Understanding LO 5, 6, 7; Exploring and Using LO 8, 9, 14

Sight Words | all, look, is, her, there, we

A Listen to your teacher.

look	all	there	we

is	her	we	all

is	look	there	her

B Read each sentence. Match it to the correct picture.

Look at her bed.

There is the stool.

We all ran into the kitchen.

- Look at the beds. Ring the word 'all'. Ring the word 'there'.
- Look at the armchairs. Put an X on the word 'is'. Put an X on the word 'we'.
- Look at the baths. Put a dot on the word 'her'. Put a dot on the word 'look'.

Phonics ch, sh, th, wh

A Can you match each picture to the correct sound?

ch

sh

th

wh

B Read each sentence. Match it to the correct picture.

I put the chair in the shed.

The shampoo is on the bath.

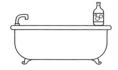

The brush is in the bin.

The pot is on the cooker.

How do I feel about my work today?

Strand: Reading **Element:** Understanding LO 5

Phonics – Write Words | ch, sh, th, oo (book), oo (tooth), ou, er

A Ring the correct word. Write it.

mat mop 	bed bath 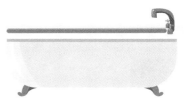
stool shed 	bin bench 
roof room 	shelf shampoo 
cooker couch 	ketchup kitchen 

How do I feel about my work today?

Strand: Reading **Element:** Understanding LO 5 **Strand:** Writing **Element:** Understanding LO 4

Grammar – Capital Letters 1

A Match each capital letter to its lower case letter.

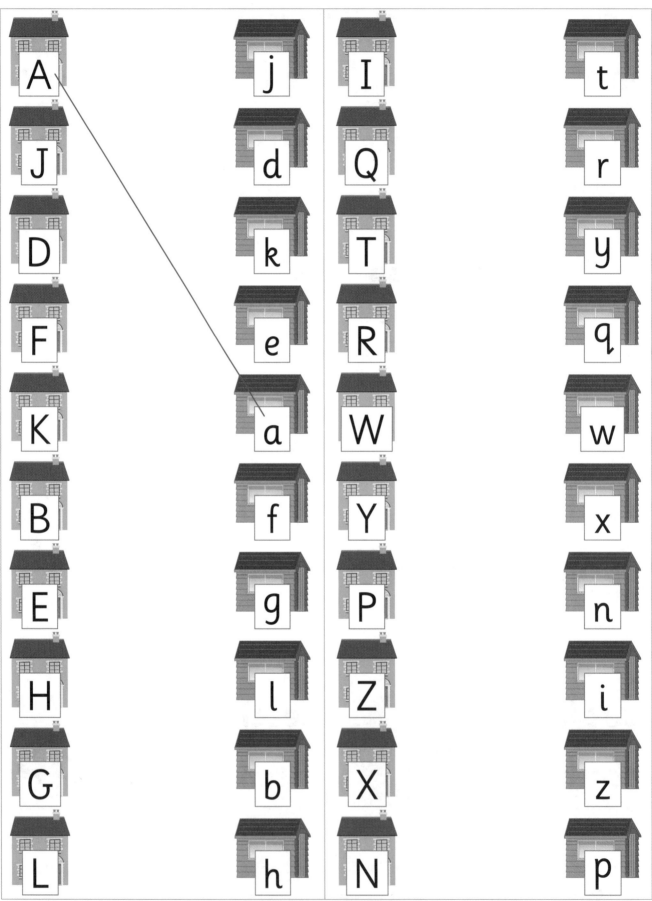

A   J   D   F   K   B   E   H   G   L

j   d   k   e   a   f   g   l   b   h

I   Q   T   R   W   Y   P   Z   X   N

t   r   y   q   w   x   n   i   z   p

How do I feel about my work today?

Strand: Writing **Element:** Understanding LO 3

Writing Genre – Parts of a Narrative

A The Three Little Pigs

In pairs, retell the story. Number the pictures in the correct order. Number 1 has been done for you.

B Interview a character from the story.

One pupil sits in the hot seat and pretends to be a character from the story while the class ask them questions.

Strand: Reading Element: Exploring and Using LO 8, 9
Strand: Oral Language Element: Exploring and Using LO 8, 9

Goldilocks and the Three Bears

10

Oral Language – Sequencing

A Goldilocks and the Three Bears

In pairs, retell the story. Number the pictures in the correct order. Number 1 has been done for you.

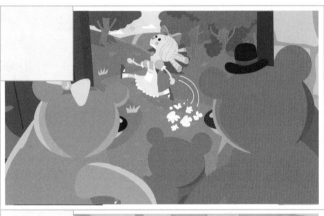

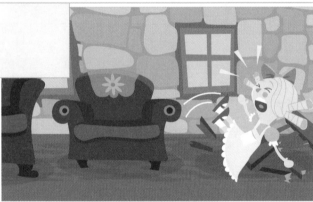

B Interview a character from the story.

One pupil sits in the hot seat and pretends to be a character from the story while the class ask them questions.

Strand: Oral Language **Element:** Exploring and Using LO 8, 9, 11

Sight Words   have, be, go, some, am, then

A Listen to your teacher.

 **be**    **go**    **have**    **am**

 **then**    **have**    **some**    **be**

 **go**    **am**    **then**    **some**

B Read each sentence. Match it to the correct picture.

I am sad.

We will all go to the shop.

Can I have some sweets?

- Look at the gardens. Ring the word 'am'. Ring the word 'be'.
- Look at the garages. Put an X on the word 'some'. Put an X on the word 'have'.
- Look at the houses. Put a dot on the word 'go'. Put a dot on the word 'then'.

Phonics – Read Sentences ai, ee, oo (tooth), or, sh, th

A Look at the picture above. Read each sentence and tick (✓) 'yes' or 'no'.

1.	The stool is on the mat.	**Yes**	**No**
2.	The brush is in the shed.	**Yes**	**No**
3.	The rubbish is in the bin.	**Yes**	**No**
4.	The bath is in the garden.	**Yes**	**No**
5.	The cat is asleep on the roof.	**Yes**	**No**
6.	The torch is on the chair.	**Yes**	**No**

How do I feel about my work today?

Strand: Reading Element: Understanding LO 5

Phonics – Write Words ee, or, sh, th

A Look at each picture. Write the word.

_____ _____ _____

_____ _____ _____

_____ _____ _____

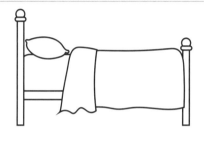

_____ _____ _____

_____ _____ _____

_____ _____ _____

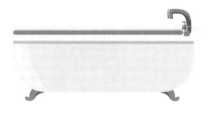

_____ _____ _____

_____ _____ _____

How do I feel about my work today?

Strand: Reading **Element:** Understanding LO 5 **Strand:** Writing **Element:** Understanding LO 4

Grammar – Capital Letters 2

A Write the lower case letter beside each capital letter.

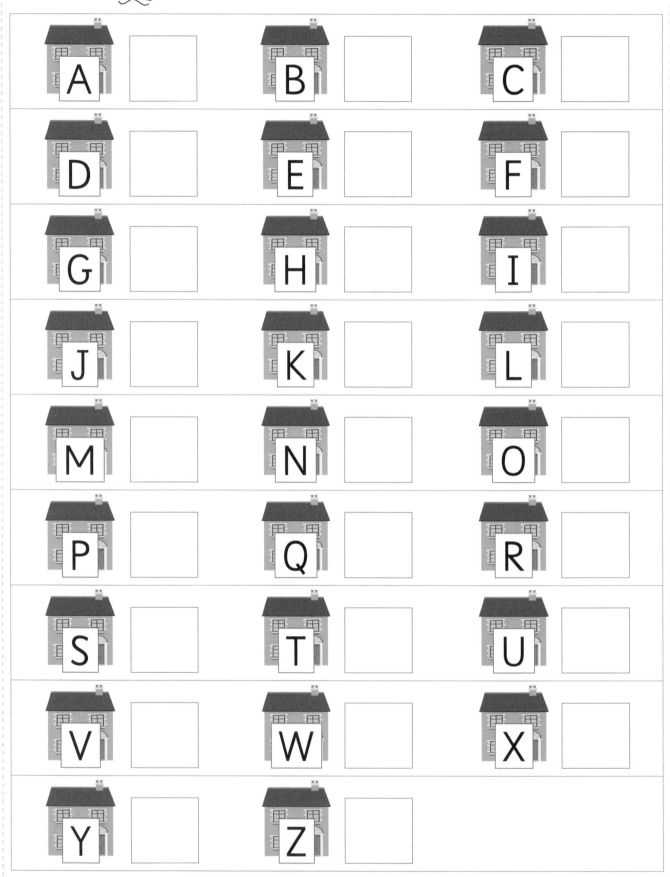

A

B

C

D

E

F

G

H

I

J

K

L

M

N

O

P

Q

R

S

T

U

V

W

X

Y

Z

How do I feel about my work today?

Strand: Writing **Element:** Understanding LO 3

Writing Genre – Modelled Writing

A **Goldilocks and the Three Bears** 🖍

In pairs, add labels to the story.

Strand: Writing **Elements:** Communicating LO 1; Understanding LO 3, 4; Exploring and Using LO 6

The Sports Shop

11

Oral Language

A Talk about the picture.

A

Strand: Oral Language **Elements:** Understanding LO 5, 6, 7; Exploring and Using LO 8, 9, 14

Sight Words – Revision Sentences

A Unscramble the sentences.

1. is a cat that

That _____

2. at look the snails

_____

3. we sweets have some

_____

4. is no coffee there

_____

5. I the shop go to

_____

Phonics – Write Words | CVC, oa, ie oo (tooth)

A Look at each picture. Write the word.

_____ _____ _____

_____ _____ _____

_____ _____ _____

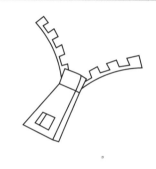

_____ _____ _____

_____ _____ _____ _____

_____ _____ _____

_____ _____ _____

_____ _____ _____

How do I feel about my work today?

Strand: Writing **Element:** Understanding LO 4

Phonics – Read Sentences | ai, oa, ie, ee, ng, oo (tooth), ue

A Read each sentence. Tick (✓) the correct picture.

1. Hang up your hat.

2. Mum had a big, red bag.

3. Dad put on a blue tie.

4. The man had a cap and a hat.

5. She spilled paint on her coat.

6. Dan had a pair of green boots.

7. I got a hat and a scarf in the shop.

How do I feel about my work today?

Strand: Reading Element: Understanding LO 5

Grammar – Capital Letters 3

A Write the capital letter beside each lower case letter.

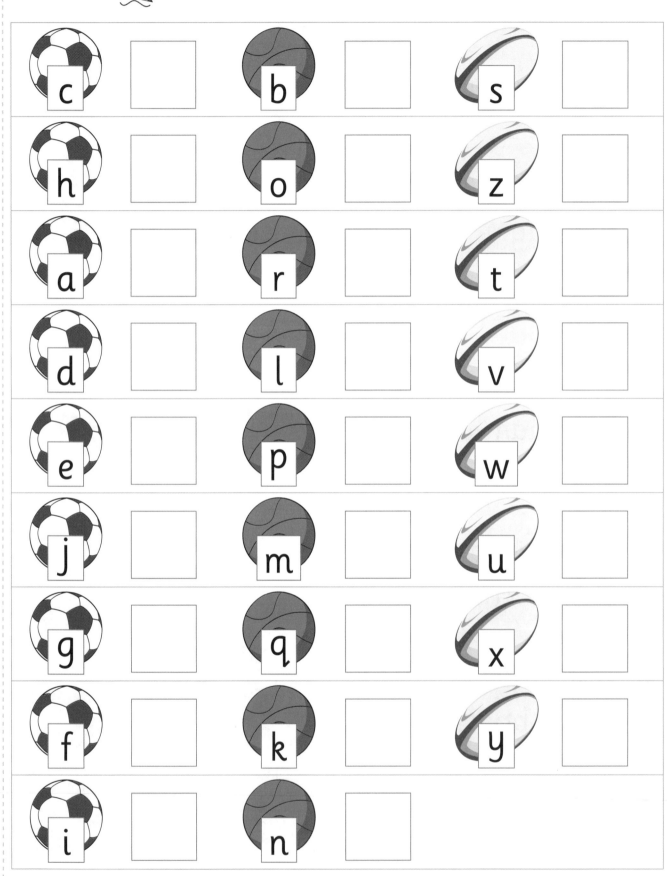

How do I feel about my work today?

Strand: Writing **Element:** Understanding LO 3

Writing Genre – Shared Writing

A The Elves and the Shoemaker

 Vocab

In pairs, draw a picture book illustrating the story of 'The Elves and the Shoemaker'. Add labels.

1.

2.

3.

4.

Strand: Writing Elements: Communicating LO 1; Understanding LO 3, 4, 5; Exploring and Using LO 6, 7

Who, Where, When

Oral Language

A Look at each box. Match the correct pictures to 'who', 'where' and 'when'.

emperor

Who?

palace

man

boy

house

servant

workshop

Where?

emperor

farm

house of straw

palace

last night

When?

Christmas

today

this morning

cottage

Strand: Oral Language **Element:** Exploring and Using LO 10

Sight Words little, down, do, can, me, are

A Listen to your teacher.

 down

 do

 are

 me

 can

 little

 do

 me

 little

 down

 do

 can

B Read each sentence. Match it to the correct picture.

I must bend down.

We have three little pups.

Can you do that for me?

- Look at the football jerseys. Ring the word 'me'. Ring the word 'are'.
- Look at the basketballs. Put an X on the word 'can'. Put an X on the word 'little'.
- Look at the tennis racquets. Put a dot on the word 'do'. Put a dot on the word 'down'.

Strand: Reading **Element:** Understanding LO 5

Phonics – Revision | ai, oa, ie, ee, or, ng, oo (book), oo (tooth), ou, oi, ue, er, ar

A Look at each picture. Write the sound that you hear in each word. ✏️

ai   oa   ie   ee

oo

We can make the /u/ sound as in '**book**' or the /ue/ sound as in '**tooth**'.

or   ng   oo   oo

ou   oi   ue   er   ar

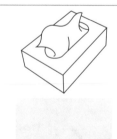

How do I feel about my work today? 🙂 ⚪ 😐 ⚪ ☹️ ⚪

Strand: Reading **Element:** Understanding LO 5 **Strand:** Writing **Element:** Exploring and Using LO 9

Phonics – Revision – Read Sentences

A Read each sentence. Tick (✓) the correct picture.

1. I can count to ten.

2. Put the coins in the bag.

3. Dad got a pot of glue.

4. The dog ran around the park.

5. The cat bit the dog's tail.

6. The toad hid in the mud.

7. The jeep got a flat wheel.

How do I feel about my work today? 🙂 ⚪ 😐 ⚪ 🙁 ⚪

Strand: Reading **Element:** Understanding LO 5

Grammar – Capital Letters and Full Stops 1

A Read each sentence. Tick it (✓) if it is correct.

1.		I like your coat. ✓
2.		Pat has a red hat
3.		Anna put on her scarf.
4.		Sam has a blue cap
5.		dad put on his tie.
6.		Tim got a pair of boots.
7.		Ella got runners in the shop

How do I feel about my work today?

Strand: Writing Element: Understanding LO 3

Writing Genre – Independent Writing

A The Emperor's New Clothes

Vocab

Draw a picture book illustrating the story of 'The Emperor's New Clothes'. Add labels.

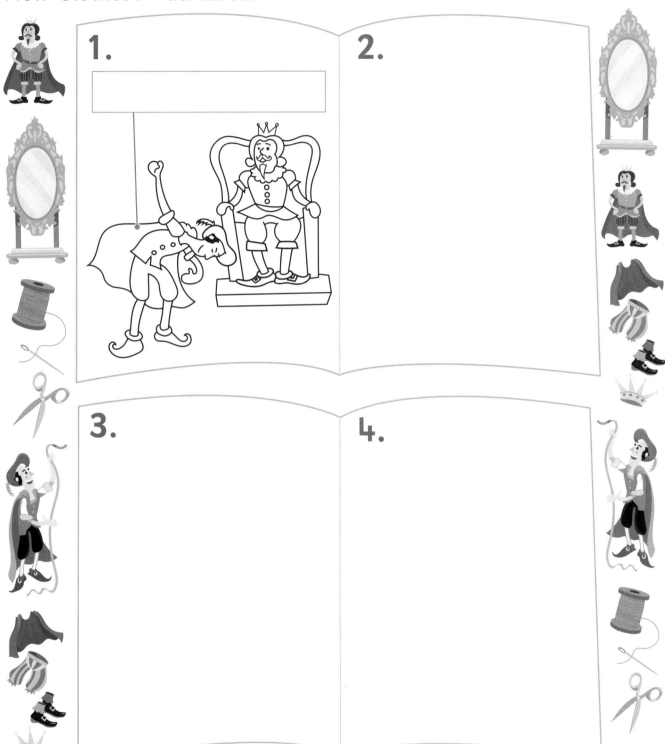

B Make a recording.

Record the pupils telling the story in their own words. Replay it and check that they remembered when, who, where and what.

Strand: Reading **Elements:** Communicating LO 1; Understanding LO 3, 4, 5; Exploring and Using LO 6, 7

The Garden Centre

13

Oral Language

A Talk about the picture.

plants

shed

soil

Garden Centre
Open 8 o'clock to 6 o'clock

Please pay here

All seeds €2

trees

pots

Trees €10

Bushes €5

Plants €2

Strand: Oral Language **Elements:** Understanding LO 5, 6, 7; Exploring and Using LO 8, 9, 14

Sight Words — your, come, here, no, so, my

A Listen to your teacher.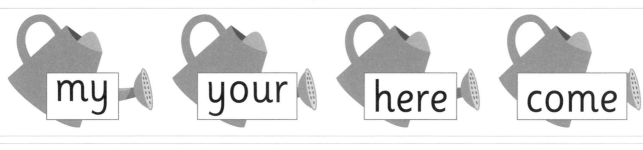

 my
 your
 here
 come

 no
 so
 here
 your

so
my
here
no

B Read each sentence. Match it to the correct picture.

I put my coat on.

Your dad said, "Come here."

I will jump up and down.

- Look at the watering cans. Ring the word 'come'. Ring the word 'your'.
- Look at the hoses. Put an X on the word 'so'. Put an X on the word 'no'.
- Look at the bird houses. Put a dot on the word 'here'. Put a dot on the word 'my'.

Phonics – Story – Dig, Dig, Dig

A Read the story.

Dig, Dig, Dig

1.

Tess gets a pot and some seeds.

2.

She wants to plant the seeds.

3.

She needs some soil. She digs and digs!

4.

Then, she puts the soil and the seeds into the pot.

5.

Soon Tess has some green plants!

How do I feel about my work today?

Strand: Reading Element: Understanding LO 5

Phonics – Questions – Dig, Dig, Dig

A Tick (✓) the real word.

	sul soil		pot put
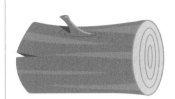	log lug		deg dig
	plont plant		grass gross

B Tick (✓) the correct sentence.

1.		Tess gets some sweets. Tess gets some seeds.
2.		Tess puts soil into the pot. Tess puts soil into the pan.
3.		Tess digs in the shop. Tess digs in the garden.

How do I feel about my work today?

Strand: Reading **Element:** Understanding LO 5

Grammar – Capital Letters and Full Stops 2

A Rewrite each sentence. Add a capital letter and a full stop.

1. mum cut the grass

_____

2. adam likes to dig

_____

3. hana got some seeds

_____

4. we have a garden

_____

5. that is a big pot

_____

How do I feel about my work today? ○ ○ ○

Strand: Writing Element: Understanding LO 3

Writing Genre – Parts of a Report

A Game: Which bug am I?

Pick one of the bugs below, but don't tell the class. Give lots of clues. Be sure to tell them:

- if it is or isn't an insect.
- what it looks like.
- where it lives.
- what it eats.

B Try playing the game in pairs.

Strand: Oral Language Elements: Understanding LO 5, 6, 7; Exploring and Using LO 13

'Sunflowers'

Oral Language – Artwork

A Talk about the picture.

'Sunflowers' by Vincent van Gogh

Strand: Oral Language **Elements:** Understanding LO 5, 6, 7; Exploring and Using LO 8, 9, 14

Sight Words – Revision Phrases

A Play the game.

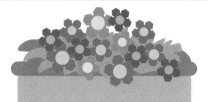

1.

come here

you have

2.

there is

we are

3.

I have a

stop me

4.

I will go

look at me

5.

he said that

you have

6.

look at the

this is my

- Play the game in pairs. You will need 12 counters each and a die.
- The player who rolls the highest number goes first.
- Throw the die and read a phrase from the flower box with the number rolled. If read correctly, place your counter on the phrase.
- The player who covers all phrases first wins.
- Variation: Can you put the phrases in a sentence this time?

Phonics – Read Sentences

ee, ng, oo (book), oo (tooth), ou, oi

A Read each sentence. Match it to the correct picture.

The bell went ding dong.

I like to swim in the pool.

Your teeth are in your mouth.

Dad put a red sheet on the bed.

Ted put the book up on the shelf.

The vet put the horse in the hut.

Gran put the can of oil in the shed.

How do I feel about my work today?

Strand: Reading Element: Understanding LO 5

Phonics – Write Words | ai, oa, ee, ng, or, sh, th, wh

A Look at each picture. Write the word.

_ _ _ _ _

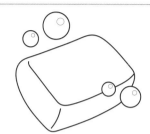

_ _ _ _

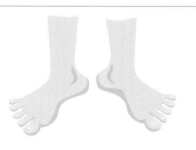

_ _ _ _

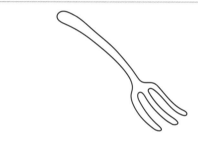

_ _ _ _

_ _ _ _

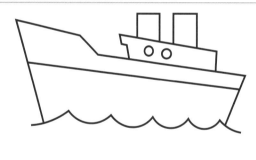

_ _ _ _

_ _ _ _

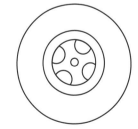

_ _ _ _ _

How do I feel about my work today?

Strand: Writing **Element:** Understanding LO 4

Grammar – Capital Letters and Full Stops 3

A Rewrite each sentence. Add a capital letter and a full stop.

1. a bee buzzed past

_____

2. ben stood on a slug

_____

3. i saw a bug on a log

_____

4. snails like to eat plants

_____

5. ants like to eat seeds

How do I feel about my work today?

Strand: Writing **Element:** Understanding LO 3

Writing Genre – Modelled and Shared Writing

A Random fact sheet

Match each fact about the snail to the correct box.

The Snail

eats plants and leaves

is not an insect

hard shell on its back

lives in gardens

What is it?

Looks like

Lives

Eats

B With your class, write a report about the snail.

Oral Language

A Talk about the picture.

seal

monkey

rhino

zookeeper

giraffe

ZOO

Tickets

Strand: Oral Language **Elements:** Understanding LO 5, 6, 7; Exploring and Using LO 8, 9, 14

Sight Words | one, by, like, want, I'm, too

A Listen to your teacher.

 like    one    I'm    want

 by    want    too    I'm

 like    one   by    too

B Colour the correct sentence for each picture.

I want a football too.

I want a fork too.

Do you like green?

Do you like blue?

- Look at the zebras. Ring the word 'one'. Ring the word 'I'm'.
- Look at the elephants. Put an X on the word 'by'. Put an X on the word 'want'.
- Look at the giraffes. Put a dot on the word 'too'. Put a dot on the word 'like'.

Phonics – Read Sentences ai, oa, ie, ee, ng, oi, ar, ch, sh

A Read each sentence. Fill in the correct word.

1.	The dog has a big _____ .	toilet / tail
2.	The _____ hid in the mud.	toad / toast
3.	I hit my leg and I _____ .	cried / chips
4.	Can I keep the bag of _____ ?	sweets / shark
5.	The _____ sang a sad song.	king / kitten
6.	Dad got _____ in the shop.	farm / fish

How do I feel about my work today?

Strand: Reading Element: Understanding LO 5 Strand: Writing Element: Exploring and Using LO 9

Grammar – Capital Letters and Full Stops 4

A Unscramble each sentence. Add a capital letter and a full stop. ✎

1. lion the roars

_____

2. hippo the can swim

_____

3. big the ostrich runs

_____

4. monkey the bananas eats

_____

5. jumps the kangaroo around

_____

How do I feel about my work today?

Writing Genre – Independent Writing

A Random fact sheet

Match each fact about the ostrich to the correct box.

The Ostrich

lives in deserts and zoos

eats roots, seeds and insects

is a bird

has long legs, a long neck and wings

What is it?

Looks like

Lives

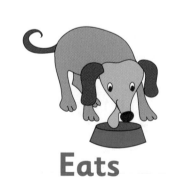

Eats

B Write a report about the ostrich by yourself.
Include a title and four sentences.

Strand: Writing **Elements:** Understanding LO 3, 4, 5; Exploring and Using LO 6, 7

The Ice-cream Parlour 16

Oral Language

A Talk about the picture.

menu

Ice-cream

Small tub €1   Large tub €2

Small cone €1   Large cone €2

Drinks

Water €1   Slushy €2   Milkshake €2

cones

slushy

customer

server

tubs

Tips, please!

Chocolate   Strawberry   Banana   Mint

ice-cream

Strand: Oral Language **Elements:** Understanding LO 5, 6, 7; Exploring and Using LO 8, 9, 14

Phonics – Story – Fun Fred

A Read the story.

Fun Fred

1.

This is Fun Fred.

2.

He works in an ice-cream van.

3.

All of the children want ice-cream, all day long.

4.

Oops! This is too much ice-cream!

5.

"I'm fed up of this job!"

How do I feel about my work today?

Strand: Reading Element: Understanding LO 5

Phonics – Questions – Fun Fred

A Tick (✓) the real word.

	ven van		nuts nots
	shup shop		tub tud
	mess miss		scoop sceep

B Tick (✓) the correct sentence.

1. 	Fred works in a shop. Fred works in a van.
2. 	The children want chips. The children want ice-cream.
3.	Fred does not like his job. Fred likes his job.

How do I feel about my work today?

Strand: Reading Element: Understanding LO 5

Sight Words · could, would, should, before, what, their

A Listen to your teacher.

| could | would | their | before |

| what | should | before | would |

| could | what | their | should |

B Read each sentence. Match it to the correct picture.

They went to visit their gran.

We had sweets before dinner.

I could not go to the park.

- Look at the ice-cream cones. Ring the word 'before'. Ring the word 'their'.
- Look at the ice-pops. Put an X on the word 'would'. Put an X on the word 'what'.
- Look at the milkshakes. Put a dot on the word 'should'. Put a dot on the word 'could'.

Strand: Reading Element: Understanding LO 5

Grammar – Capital Letters and Full Stops 5

A Unscramble each sentence. Add a capital letter and a full stop.

1. like ice-cream I

_____

2. hot it is very

_____

3. melted the ice-cream

_____

4. got an ice-pop I

_____

5. see I van the ice-cream

_____

How do I feel about my work today?

Writing Genre – Independent Writing

A Ice-cream

Discuss with your class how ice-cream looks, smells, feels and tastes. Then, draw pictures and label them.

Looks like…

Smells like…

Feels like…

Tastes like…

B Now, write a poem.

Ice-cream

Looks like

Smells like

Feels like

Tastes like

By

Strand: Writing **Elements:** Understanding LO 3, 4, 5; Exploring and Using LO 6

The Ice-cream Van

Oral Language – Spot the Differences

A Look carefully at the pictures. Can you spot 6 differences?

Ice-cream van A

Ice-cream van B

Sight Words – Sight-word Phrases

A Play the game.

1.

I could
he would

2.

should you
before that

3.

would you like
do you want

4.

could I have
what do you

5.

are we there
look at their

6.

he said no
could she go

- Play the game in pairs. You will need 12 counters each and a die.
- The player who rolls the highest number goes first.
- Throw the die and read a phrase from the ice-cream stand with the number rolled. If read correctly, place your counter on the phrase.
- The player who covers all phrases first wins.
- Variation: Can you put the phrases in a sentence this time?

Strand: Reading Element: Understanding LO 5

Phonics – Revision – Write CVC Words

A Look at each picture. Write the word.

How do I feel about my work today?

Strand: Writing **Element:** Understanding LO 4

Phonics – Revision – Write Words with Digraphs

A Look at each picture. Write the word.

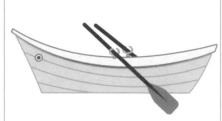

b___ ___ t

m___ ___th

cl___ ___

h___ n

c___ n

d___ ___t

ki___ ___

b___ ___k

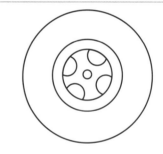

wh___ ___l

t___ ___

r___ ___n

mix___ ___

How do I feel about my work today?

Strand: Writing **Element:** Understanding LO 4

Grammar – Revision – Capital Letters

A Finish the alphabet with capital letters.

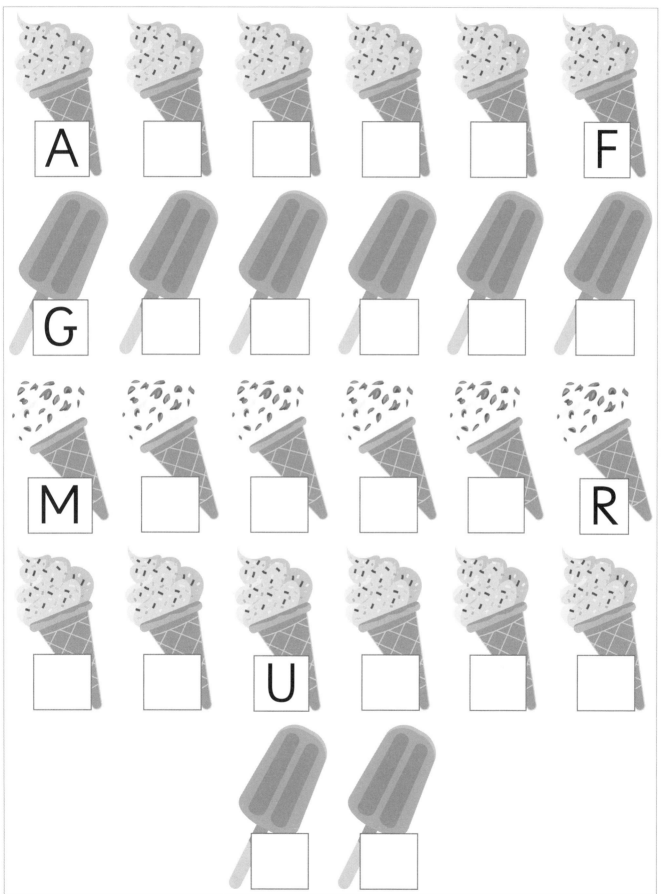

A [ ] [ ] [ ] [ ] F

G [ ] [ ] [ ] [ ] [ ]

M [ ] [ ] [ ] [ ] R

[ ] [ ] U [ ] [ ] [ ]

[ ] [ ]

How do I feel about my work today? ◯ ◯ ◯

Strand: Writing **Element:** Understanding LO 3

Assessment

Phonics Assessment

A Say each word. Write the first and final sounds that you hear. ✏️

How do I feel about my work today?

Phonics Assessment

A Say each word. Write the first and final sounds that you hear. ✏️

Phonics Assessment

A Say each word. Write the sound that you hear.

ie   ee   ai   or

 | | |

oa   ng   oo   ou

 |  | |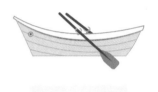

ar   oi   oo   ue   er

 |  | | |

ch   sh   th   wh

 | |  |

How do I feel about my work today?